SPACE SCHOOL

Contents

Simon Cheshire

Story illustrated by
Pet Gotohda

Heinemann

Before Reading

In this story

Ziggy

Pod

Miss West

The children

Tricky words

- mission
- ourselves
- costume
- welcome
- solar system
- whispered

Story starter

Ziggy and Pod are aliens. They have been sent to Earth to find out how humans live. This time their mission is to find out about Earth school. They dress up as school children and join a Science lesson about space travel to the planets.

Aliens at School

Ziggy and Pod had dressed up as school children.

"Our mission today is to find out about Earth school," said Ziggy.

"OK, boss," said Pod.

Ziggy and Pod went into the playground.

"First," said Ziggy, "we must give ourselves human names."

Pod looked around.

"I know, boss. You can be Way In and I will be Way Out," he said.

"Is my human costume OK?" asked Pod. "I have got one head, two arms and four legs."

Why did they choose these names?

"You fool!" said Ziggy.
"How many times have I told you?
Humans have one head, two arms
and ***two*** legs."
"Sorry, boss," said Pod.

Ziggy and Pod went into the classroom.

"Welcome to our school,"

said Miss West, the teacher.

"What are your names?"

"My name is Way In," said Ziggy.

"My name is Way Out," said Pod.

"What odd names," said Miss West.

“Today we are doing Science,” said Miss West. “We will learn about Space and the planets. There are nine planets in our solar system.”

"No!" cried Pod.

"Do not call out, Way Out," said Miss West. "Please put up your hand."

"How odd," thought Pod. "Earth children have to put up their hands to make their mouths work!"

Ziggy put up his hand.

"Yes?" said Miss West.

"There are more than nine planets in this solar system!" said Ziggy.

"You forgot about the planets Beta and Zebulon!"

Miss West was cross. "Don't be silly.
There are no such places," she said.
"Yes there are. We've been there!"
said Pod.
The children all looked at Ziggy
and Pod.

"Shhh!" whispered Ziggy to Pod.
"Humans might not know about
Beta and Zebulon."

Pod put up his hand.
"Sorry, Miss! We made it up.
We have NOT been to other planets."

Why doe
Pod chan
his min

"We use rockets to get to the planets,"
said Miss West.
Ziggy put his hand up.
"But rockets are so slow," he said.
"Why not use space-warp engines?"

Miss West was cross.
“Don’t be silly, Way In, there are no such things,” she said.
The children looked at Ziggy and Pod and giggled.

"Look at this rocket launch,"
said Miss West.
"What is that door?" asked Ziggy.
"It's the way in, Way In," said
Miss West.
"What is that up at the top?"
asked Pod.
"It's the way out, Way Out,"
said Miss West.
All the children fell about laughing!

After the lesson, Ziggy and Pod went back to their spaceship to write their mission report.

MISSION REPORT TO HOME PLANET

Visit to Earth School

Today we saw a Science lesson.
Earth teachers have never heard of the planets Beta or Zebulon!
Or space-warp engines!
They are not very clever.

Quiz

Text Detective

- Why did Ziggy and Pod think the children had to put up their hands?
- Would you like to have Ziggy and Pod in your class?

Word Detective

- **Phonic Focus**: Adding 'ing' to verbs ending in 'e'
  Page 4: Which letter must be dropped from 'give' before adding 'ing'?
- Page 4: Why do the words 'Way In' and 'Way Out' start with capital letters?
- Page 11: Find a word meaning angry.

Super Speller

Read these words:

giving children forgot

Now try to spell them!

HA! HA! HA!

Q Where do aliens park their flying saucers?

A At a parking meteor!

Before Reading

Find out about

- Astronauts who have travelled to the Moon

Tricky words

- astronauts
- travelled
- Lunar Module
- photos
- special
- gravity
- dangerous

Text starter

Astronauts have landed on the Moon but not on any other planets. The first men on the Moon were Neil Armstrong and Buzz Aldrin. But space travel is very dangerous. Would you dare to travel in a rocket?

Life in Space

Would you dare to travel in Space?
People who travel in Space are
called astronauts.
Astronauts have landed on the Moon,
but so far they have not landed
on any planets.

Apollo 11

Astronauts travel into Space in rockets.
The rocket which took the first astronauts to the Moon was called Apollo 11.
It took off in July 1969, and took four days to get to the Moon.

Three astronauts travelled into Space in Apollo 11.
Then two of the astronauts – Neil Armstrong and Buzz Aldrin – used a small spaceship to land on the Moon. The spaceship was called the Lunar Module.

First Man on the Moon

Neil Armstrong was the first man to walk on the Moon. He said, "It's one small step for a man, one giant leap for mankind." Over 500 million people on Earth watched him on TV.

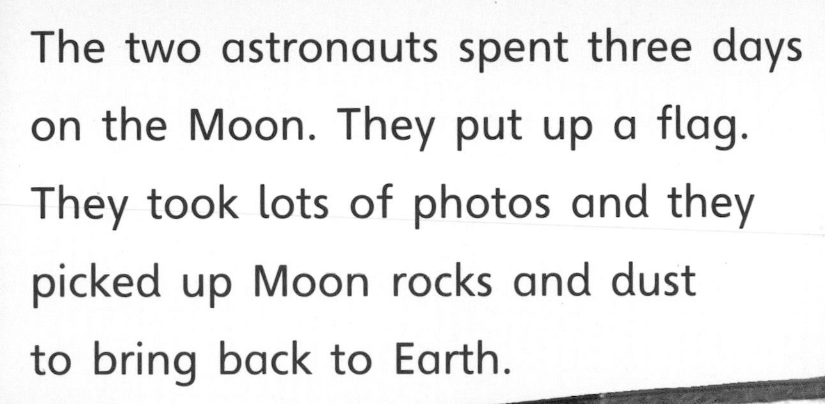

The two astronauts spent three days on the Moon. They put up a flag. They took lots of photos and they picked up Moon rocks and dust to bring back to Earth.

Walking on the Moon

So far twelve astronauts have walked on the Moon. (They were all men!)
On one flight to the Moon, the astronauts took a car!
The car was called the Moon Buggy.

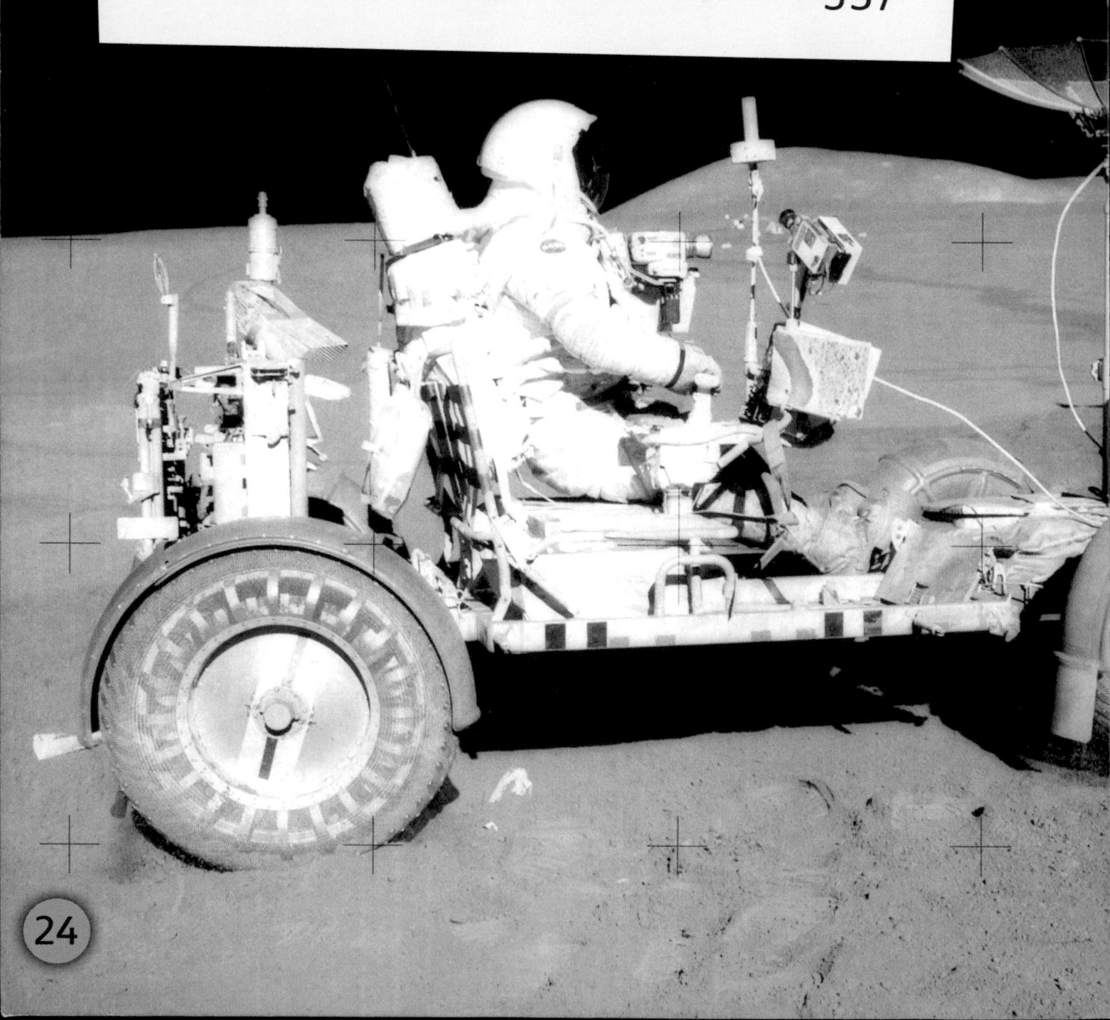

The Moon Buggy had special wheels to help it go over the Moon dust. The Moon Buggy was left on the Moon. It is still there today!

Life on the Moon

There is no weather on the Moon. There is no wind or rain, so nothing gets blown away or washed away. So the footprints left by the astronauts will be there forever!

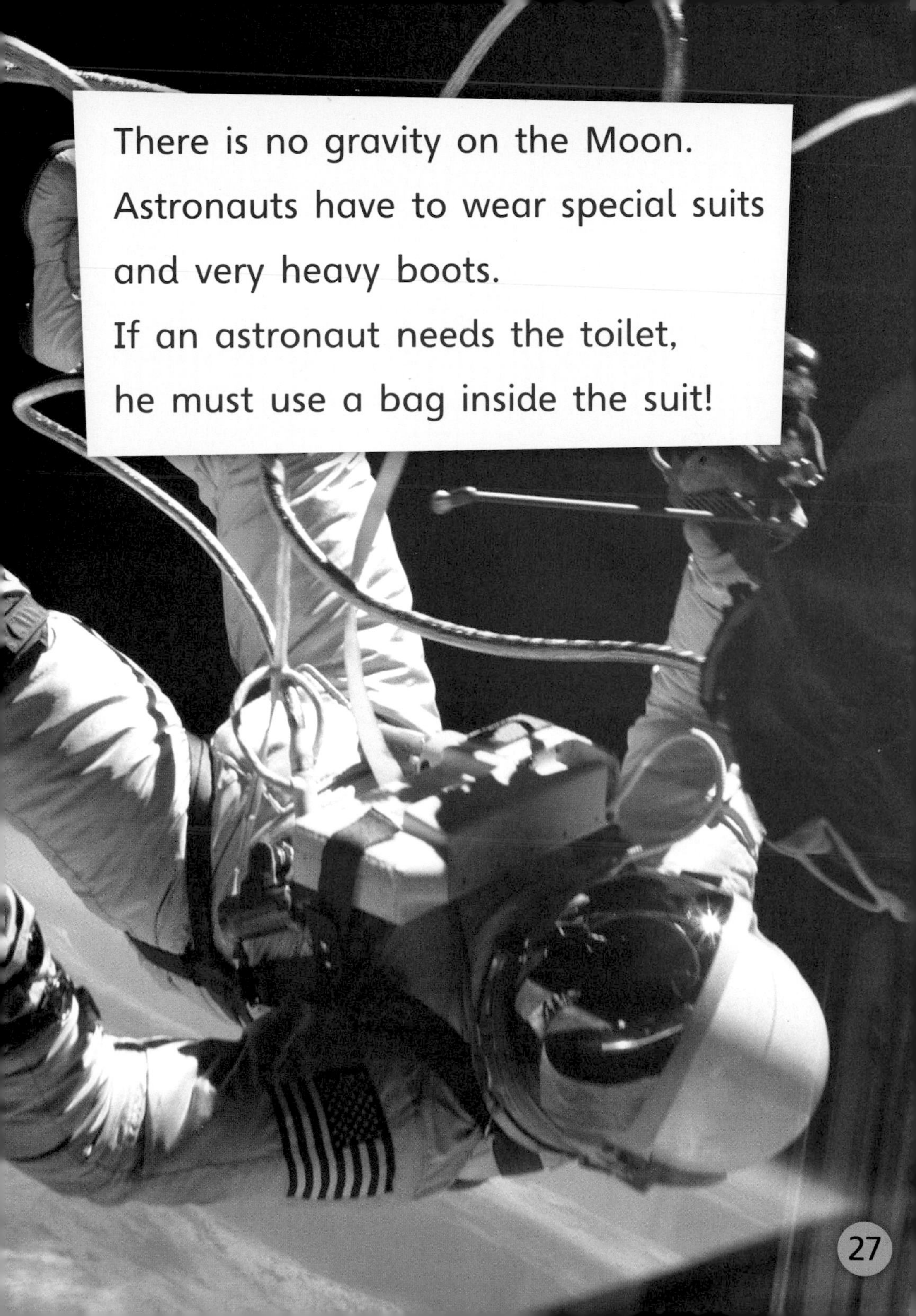

There is no gravity on the Moon.
Astronauts have to wear special suits
and very heavy boots.
If an astronaut needs the toilet,
he must use a bag inside the suit!

Life in a Spaceship

There is no gravity in a spaceship.
Everything floats around if it is
not held down.
Food is put into special bags.
Astronauts eat the food using straws.

Astronauts sleep in special bags, which stop them floating away. Astronauts can only wash using a wet sponge as the water would float away! They cannot wash their hair.

Coming back to Earth

When a rocket comes back to Earth the outside of the rocket gets very hot. It is very dangerous for the astronauts as the rocket could burn up.